a gift for us to share

to:......................................

from:....................................

OTHER HELEN EXLEY GIFTBOOKS IN THIS SERIES:
Me and my Mum
Me and my Dad
Me and my Grandma

OTHER HELEN EXLEY GIFTBOOKS:
For a wonderful Grandchild
To a very special Grandpa
To the World's best Grandpa

First published in 2006 by Helen Exley Giftbooks in
Great Britain, and Helen Exley Giftbooks LLC in the USA.
This edition published in 2010.

12 11 10 9 8 7 6 5 4 3 2 1

Illustrations © Jane Massey 2006, 2010
Copyright © Helen Exley 2006, 2010
The moral right of the author has been asserted.

ISBN 978-1-84634-525-8

Helen Exley Giftbooks,
16 Chalk Hill, Watford,
Herts WD19 4BG, UK.
www.helenexleygiftbooks.com

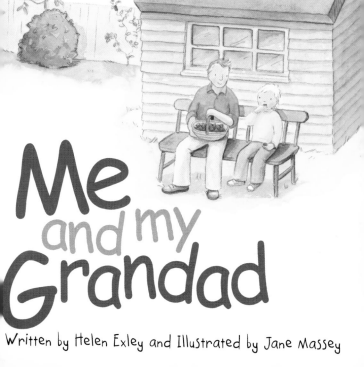

Me
and my
Grandad

Written by Helen Exley and Illustrated by Jane Massey

I love my Grandad.

And I love it most

when I stay with him.

He always waits by the window

for me to arrive.

When I stay at Grandad's
he always has a special look
in his eye, and a kind of soft smile.
I help him build things in his workshop.
We eat chocolate bars that he buys
specially for me. Usually he forgets
they're for me and eats most
of them himself.

My Grandad often shows me his family photos.

He's proud of his children and his grandchildren.

Especially me.

Grandad marks pages in his books to read with me. Did you know that he keeps hundreds and hundreds of his old books just to share with me?

One night I woke up terribly scared
because a bad bear was after me.
Grandad chased the scariness away.
He always does. He protects me
like this, and makes me feel safe.

Grandad and I often play cards together. I used to think he was a bit slow, because he always lost. But then I discovered he was letting me win because he was being kind.

Grandad tells me that he used to do
rough and tumble things with my Dad.
But now it seems they're both past it.
Grandad's still quite strong, though.
When he took me golfing, one shot broke
the clubhouse window.

Grandad's good fun, and he's game for almost anything. But he turns a bit green on round-a-bouts and swings, so then I have to look after him.

I write to my Grandad and tell him all the news. He writes back to me. It used to be to help me to learn to read but now it stops us both from being lonely.

My Grandad always, always carries my letters in his briefcase when he goes to work.

He reads them and looks at all the photos of our family.

And of me.

Grandad and I just play
and play, and talk and talk.
But then Grandad gets tired
and goes to sleep.
Then it's my turn to watch
out for him, so I have
to keep very QUIET.

Do you know that every year
Grandad grows strawberries just
for me? How can I ever say "Thank
you" for the strawberries and the
chocolates and the hugs and letters?

There are no words that
can ever say "Thank you" big enough!

WHAT IS A HELEN EXLEY GIFTBOOK?

Helen Exley Giftbooks cover the most powerful of all
human relationships: the bonds within families
and between friends, and the theme of personal values.
No expense is spared in making sure that each book
is as meaningful a gift as it is possible to create:
good to give, good to receive. You have the result
in your hands. If you have loved it – tell others!
There is no power on earth like the word-of-mouth
recommendation of friends!